Light in Our Darkness

SIMPLE CHANTS AND PSALMS

Margaret Rizza

kevin
mayhew

We hope you enjoy *Light in Our Darkness*. Further copies are available from your local Kevin Mayhew stockist.

In case of difficulty, or to request a catalogue,
please contact the publisher direct by writing to:

The Sales Department
KEVIN MAYHEW LTD
Buxhall
Stowmarket
Suffolk IP14 3BW

Phone 01449 737978
Fax 01449 737834
E-mail info@kevinmayhewltd.com

Also available:
Vocal Score   1450258
CD   1490095
Cassette   1480089

First published in Great Britain in 2002 by Kevin Mayhew Ltd.

ISBN 1 84003 913 2
ISMN M 57024 080 7
Catalogue No: 1450254

0 1 2 3 4 5 6 7 8 9

Cover design by Angela Selfe

Music setter: Geoffrey Moore
Music proof reader: Linda Ottewell

Printed and bound in Great Britain

Important Copyright Information

The Publishers wish to express their gratitude to the copyright owners who have granted permission to include their copyright material in this book. Full details are indicated on the respective pages.

The **words** of most of the songs in this publication are covered by a **Church Copyright Licence** which is available from Christian Copyright Licensing International. This allows local church reproduction on overhead projector acetates, in service bulletins, songsheets, audio/visual recording and other formats.

The **music** in this book is covered by the additional **Music Reproduction Licence** which is issued by CCLI in the territories of Europe and Australasia. You may photocopy the music and words of the songs in the book provided:

You hold a current Music Reproduction Licence from CCLI.

The copyright owner of the song you intend to photocopy is included in the Authorised Catalogue List which comes with your Music Reproduction Licence.

The Music Reproduction Licence is **not** currently available in the USA or Canada.

Full details of CCLI can be obtained from their Web site (www.ccli.com) or you can contact them direct at the following offices:

Christian Copyright Licensing (Europe) Ltd
PO Box 1339, Eastbourne, East Sussex, BN21 1AD, UK
Tel: +44 (0)1323 417711; Fax: +44 (0)1323 417722; E-mail: info@ccli.co.uk

CCL Asia-Pacific Pty Ltd (Australia and New Zealand)
PO Box 6644, Baulkham Hills Business Centre, NSW 2153, Australia
Tel: +61 (02) 9894-5386; Toll Free Phone: 1-800-635-474
Fax: +61 (02) 9894-5701; Toll Free Fax: 1-800-244-477
E-mail executive@ccli.co.au

Christian Copyright Licensing Inc
17201 NE Sacramento Street, Portland, Oregon 97230, USA
Tel: +1 (503) 257 2230; Toll Free Phone: 1 (800) 234 2446;
Fax: +1 (503) 257 2244; E-mail executive@ccli.com

Please note, all texts and music in this book are protected by copyright and if you do not possess a licence from CCLI they may not be reproduced in any way for sale or private use without the consent of the copyright owner.

About the Composer

Margaret Rizza studied at the Royal College of Music, London, and the National School of Opera, London. She completed her training in Siena and Rome.

She has sung at many of the world's leading operatic venues and under such conductors as Benjamin Britten, Igor Stravinsky and Leonard Bernstein. She was also a frequent broadcaster.

From 1977 to 1994 she taught singing at the Guildhall School of Music and Drama, London.

Since 1983 she has dedicated herself to the work of spirituality and to the wider aspect of music in the community.

She leads many retreats and choral days and is closely involved with the World Community for Christian Meditation (WCCM).

She now works full-time composing and giving retreats, prayer and music days and choral workshops.

Contents

Dedicated to Kevin Mayhew

Foreword

All that came to be had life in him and that life was the light of men, a light that shines in the dark, a light that darkness could not overpower.
John 1:4, 5 (The Jerusalem Bible)

Light in Our Darkness is a collection of Chants and Psalms. I am grateful to all those who asked me to meet a need for something which could be easily sung.

All the music is underpinned in some way by prayer and many of the pieces were birthed in the horror of 11 September 2001. How can one respond to this terrible violation of everything one holds sacred?

It seems to me and to many people that the only thing which will change and save our wonderful world is prayer and a dialogue of friendship and love between all peoples and between all religions.

Many of the Chants and Psalms are prayers of gratitude and praise, of repentance and reconciliation; a melting pot of anguish and joy, of a longing to be at one with this living light who shines in our darkness leading us into this eternal source of love and peace.

Singing These Chants

You will find that in using this music most of it can be done very simply indeed by the smallest of groups, singing in unison, or it can be expanded to incorporate much larger forces who have more diverse musical resources at their disposal.

Do be adventurous and work on variety. It is lovely to hear the different voices being highlighted, sometimes male, sometimes female, sometimes solo, sometimes children's voices; and then to hear the different colours of the various instruments – all facets of God's life, love and beauty being revealed, poured out and manifested through our musical gifts.

There will naturally be more freedom of choice in the chants which can be as short as 2-3 minutes or as long as 8-10 minutes.

I have many people to thank who have helped me during these months of writing the music: my beloved family who very often have to cope with a hermit-like wife and mother; St Thomas' Music Group and the Church with whom I have shared many things and who are such an important part of the music-making; my publisher who has always given me so much support and encouragement and to whom this collection is dedicated; the many people involved with the publishing and recording of this music; and the Christian Meditation Communities (WCCM) who over the years have become an intrinsic part of my life.

And so again my hope is that this music will be a way of prayer; a way of enabling our hearts to be open to this light, this source of all life; that we may work for peace, justice and truth; that we may be a light for those who have no hope, who have no voice and who live in darkness, that the music may bring love, joy, peace and compassion to all who sing and play it or who just sit and listen to it.

Margaret Rizza

IN GOD ALONE

Text: Psalm 61(62)
Music: Margaret Rizza

CHOIR

In God a-lone is my soul at rest; he a-lone is my rock, my strength; in God a-lone is my soul at rest; he a-lone is my rock, he is my strength. He a-lone, he is my strength.

EQUAL VOICE PARTS

In God a-lone is my soul at rest; he a-lone is my rock, my strength; in God a-lone is my soul at rest; he a-lone is my rock, he is my strength.

CHORAL ACCOMPANIMENT BACKGROUND

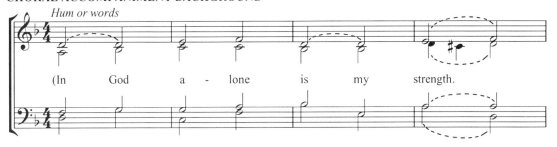

ORGAN/KEYBOARD

Simple accompaniment 1

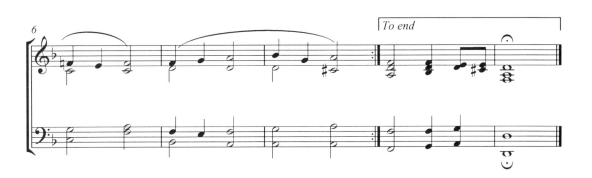

Accompaniment 2

Variation (if no C instruments are available)

INSTRUMENTAL PARTS

OBOES OR OTHER C INSTRUMENTS

FLUTES OR OTHER C INSTRUMENTS (join after oboe duet to make quartet)

C INSTRUMENTS

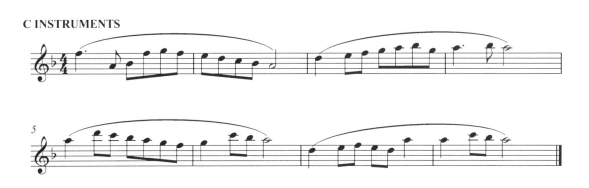

RECORDERS OR OTHER C INSTRUMENTS

CELLO
Basso continuo 1

Basso continuo 2

GUITAR

Accompaniment 1

Accompaniment 2

Light in Our
Darkness

YOUR WORD IS A LAMP

Text: from Psalm 119
Music: Margaret Rizza

Your word is a light for my path. Your

word is a lamp for my feet.

Solo or Unison

1. I have sworn and have de-

ter - mined to o - bey your just de- crees.

I am, Lord, most deep-ly af-flic-ted,

give me life, by your word, give me life.

Refrain
Instrument (optional)

Refrain
Unison or SATB

Your word is a lamp for my feet. Your

Ped.

Man.

Ped.

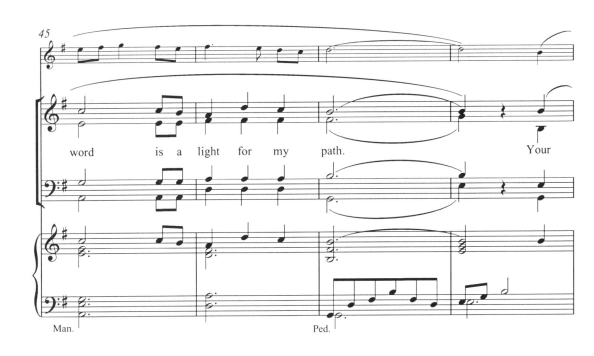

word   is   a   light   for   my   path.   Your

Man.   Ped.

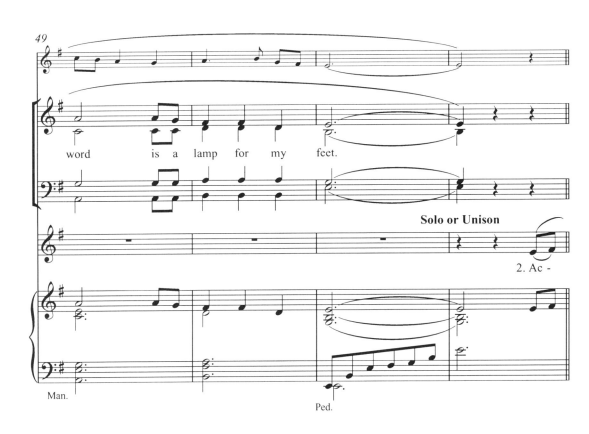

word   is   a   lamp   for   my   feet.

Solo or Unison

2. Ac -

Man.   Ped.

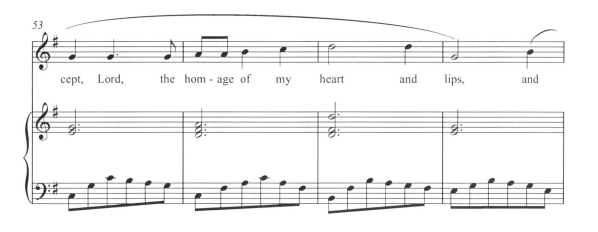

cept, Lord, the hom-age of my heart and lips, and

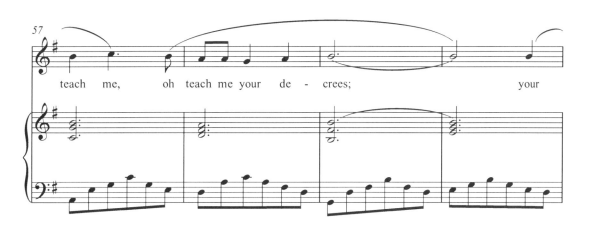

teach me, oh teach me your de - crees; your

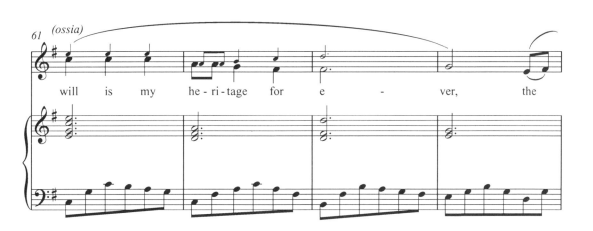

(ossia)

will is my he - ri - tage for e - ver, the

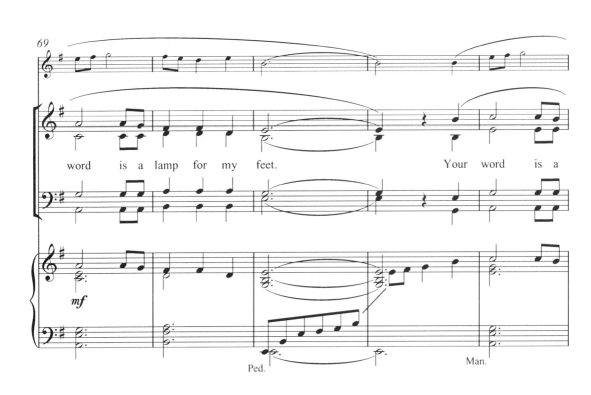

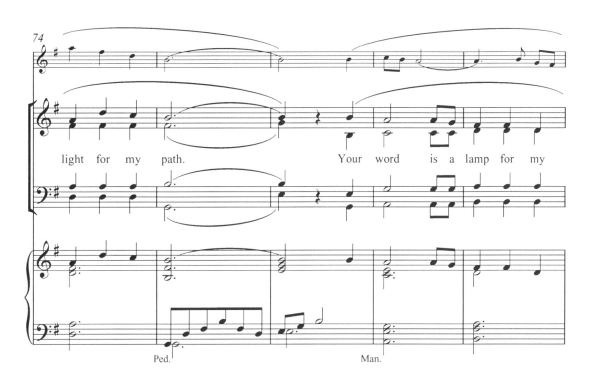

light for my path. Your word is a lamp for my

Ped. Man.

Instrument or descant (2 parts)

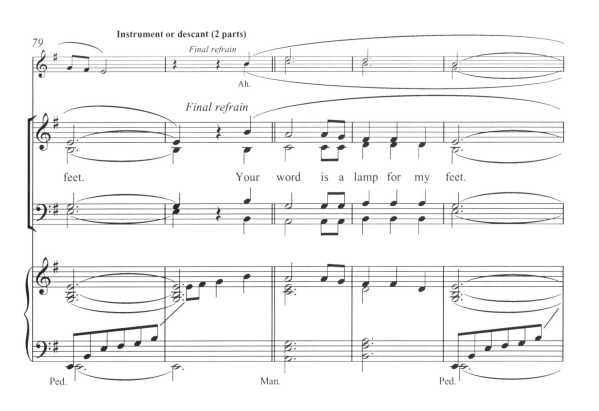

Final refrain

Ah.

Final refrain

feet. Your word is a lamp for my feet.

Ped. Man. Ped.

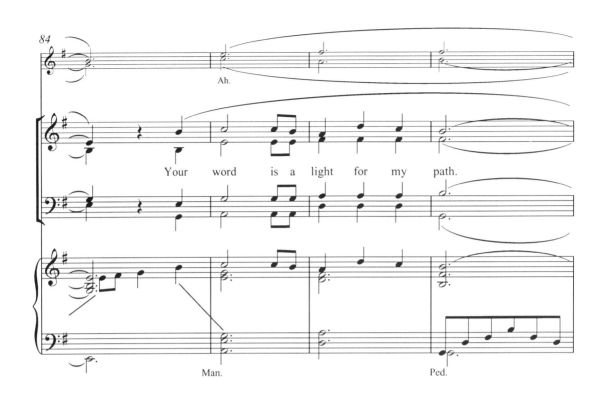

Ah.

Your word is a light for my path.

Man.

Ped.

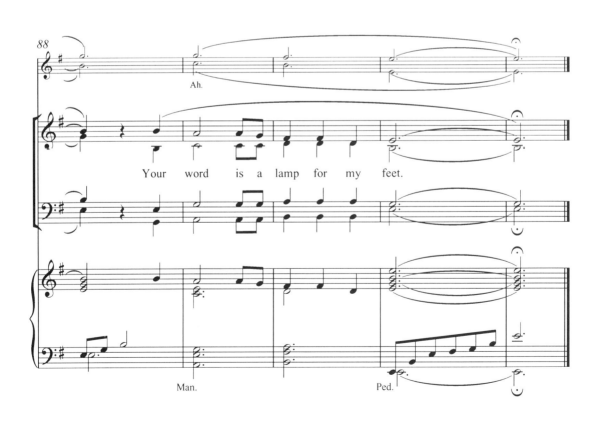

Ah.

Your word is a lamp for my feet.

Man.

Ped.

INSTRUMENTAL PARTS

MELODY INSTRUMENT (OPTIONAL)

25

CELLO PART, FOR 2 CELLI (OPTIONAL)

O GIVE THANKS TO THE LORD

Text: from Psalm 118
Music: Margaret Rizza

2. The Lord's hand has tri-umphed, his right hand raised me up, I shall not die but shall live to re-count all his deeds. O-pen to me the gates of ho-li-ness that I may en-ter giv-ing thanks to God.

3. The stone which the buil-ders re-ject-ed, has be-come for us the cor-ner-stone. This is the work of the Lord, we re-joice and are glad.

CHORAL ACCOMPANIMENT BACKGROUND

Hum or 'Ah'

Ah

Ah

ORGAN/KEYBOARD
Accompaniment 1

Accompaniment 2

Variation

INSTRUMENTAL VARIATIONS

C INSTRUMENTS

Variation 1

Variation 2

Variation 3

Duet 1

Duet 2

Duet 3

B♭ INSTRUMENT

GUITAR

Introduction only (optional)

Accompaniment chords

Variation

CELLO

Basso continuo 1

Basso continuo 2

Variation 1

Variation 2

For Pamela Hayes — written for her memorial service

THE LORD IS MY LIGHT AND MY SALVATION

Text: from Psalm 26(27), adapted from The Grail
Music: Margaret Rizza

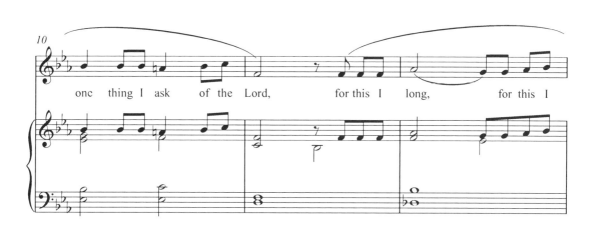

Solo or Unison

set me high up-on a rock and my head will be raised, I shall

ossia   *ossia*

of - fer now with-in his tent a sac - ri - fice of

joy.   The   Lord   is my light and my sal -

Refrain

Unison or SATB

The   Lord   is   my

O DOMINE, O CHRISTE

Text: Traditional
Music: Margaret Rizza

CHOIR, ORGAN/KEYBOARD

Unison or SATB

Translation:
O Lord, O Christ,
give us peace.

VOCAL VARIATION AND VOCAL ACCOMPANIMENT (FOR INSTRUMENTAL VARIATIONS)

Do - na no - bis pa - cem, pa - cem;

(Upper part can be used as variation)

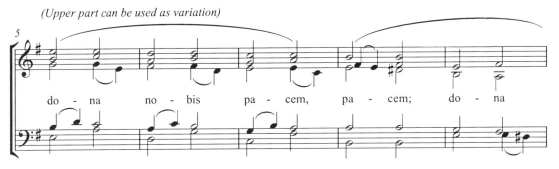

do - na no - bis pa - cem, pa - cem; do - na

no - bis pa - cem, pa - cem. pa - cem.

To repeat | Last time

OPTIONAL ORGAN/KEYBOARD INTRODUCTION (IF THERE ARE NO INSTRUMENTS)

ORGAN/KEYBOARD VARIATION (ARRANGED FROM C INSTRUMENT VARIATION)

INSTRUMENTAL PARTS

TRIO INTRODUCTION (OPTIONAL): CELLO AND C INSTRUMENTS (OR KEYBOARD)

C INSTRUMENT

B♭ INSTRUMENT

B♭ INSTRUMENT

GUITAR

Variation

CELLO
Basso continuo

For Samuel, our first grandchild

A CELTIC BLESSING

Text: Traditional
Music: Margaret Rizza

The guard-ing of the God of Life be on you, the guard-ing of lov-ing Christ be on you, the guard-ing of the Ho-ly Spi-rit be on you, to aid and up-hold you each day and night of your life; the

guard - ing of God, the guard - ing of Christ, the

guard - ing of the Ho - ly Spi - rit be up - on you.

OPTIONAL KEYBOARD INTRODUCTION (IF THERE ARE NO INSTRUMENTS)

Variation

VOCAL ACCOMPANIMENT 1

Chant

The guard-ing of the God of Life be on you, the guard-ing of lov-ing Christ be on you, the guard-ing of the Ho-ly Spi-rit be on you, to aid and up-hold you each day and night of your life;

The guard - ing of God, the guard - ing of Christ, the guard - ing of the Spi - rit be up - on you; the

VOCAL ACCOMPANIMENT 2

Chant

FLUTE OR OTHER C INSTRUMENT (OPTIONAL)
(May be played an octave lower)

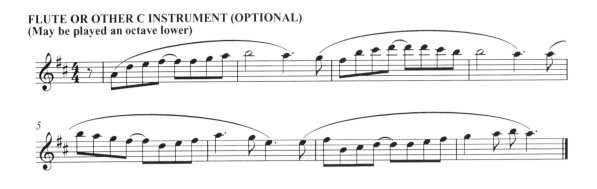

VIOLIN OR OTHER C INSTRUMENT:
Variation 1

FLUTE OR OTHER C INSTRUMENT:
Variation 2

CLARINET OR OTHER B♭ INSTRUMENT:
Introduction or Variation

CELLO: Basso continuo

CELLO: Variation 1

CELLO: Variation 2 or Introduction

CHANT FOR INSTRUMENTS

Music: Margaret Rizza

C INSTRUMENT VARIATIONS
Variation 1

Variation 2

Variation 3

Variation 4 – Duet

Variation 5

B♭ INSTRUMENT VARIATION

GUITAR
Accompaniment 1

Accompaniment 2

CELLI
Basso continuo 1

Basso continuo 2

Basso continuo 3

5

Variation 1

6

12

Variation 2

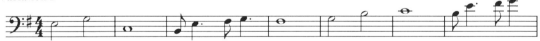

8

12

BLESS THE LORD MY SOUL

Text: from Psalm 104, Grail Translation
Music: Margaret Rizza

CHOIR, ORGAN/KEYBOARD

are; clothed in ma - jes - ty and glo - ry, wrapped in light as in a

robe.

1. You stretch out the hea-vens like a tent; a-bove the rains you build your

dwel-ling; you make the clouds your cha-ri-ot; you walk on the wings of the

2. You foun-ded the earth on its base to stand firm from age to age. You wrapped it with the o-cean like a cloak: the wa - ters stood high-er than the moun - tains.

Refrain

S
A

Bless the Lord my soul, Lord God, how great you

T
B

are; clothed in ma - jes - ty and glo - ry, wrapped in

light as in a robe.

3. You make springs gush forth in the

val - leys; they give drink to the beasts of the fields; on their

banks dwell the birds of hea - ven; from their branch-es they sing their

Unison or SATB *Refrain*

Bless the Lord my soul, Lord

song.

God, how great you are; clothed in ma - jes - ty and

glo - ry, wrapped in light as in a robe.

4. You make the grass grow for the cat - tle, and the plants to serve man's

need, that he may bring forth bread from the earth and wine to cheer man's

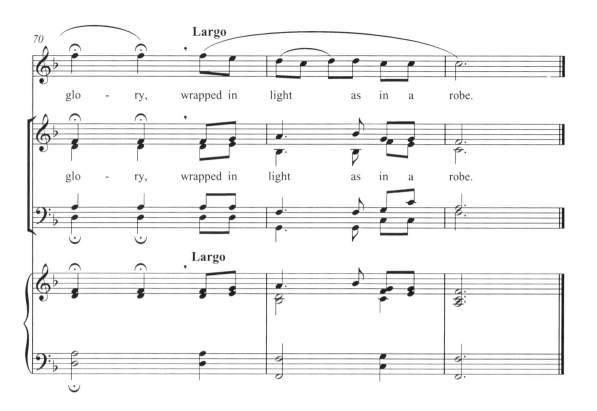

glo - ry, wrapped in light as in a robe.

glo - ry, wrapped in light as in a robe.

O LORD LISTEN TO MY PRAYER

Text: from Psalm 101(102)
Music: Margaret Rizza

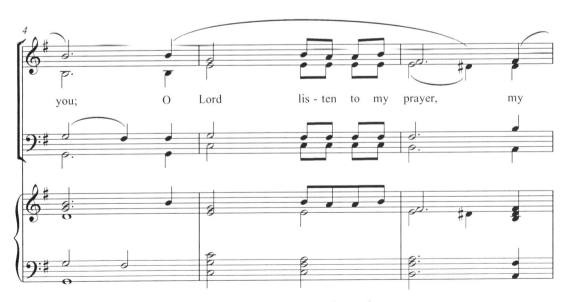

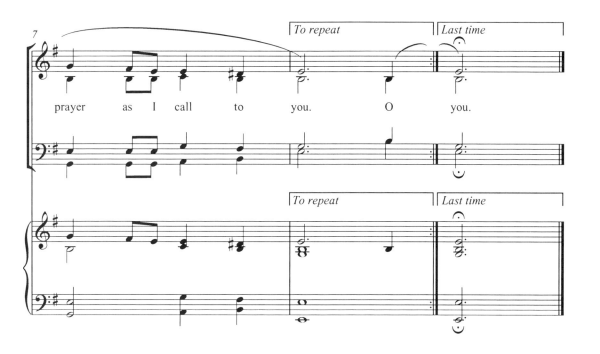

SECOND SATB VERSION (which can also be used as an ATB trio)

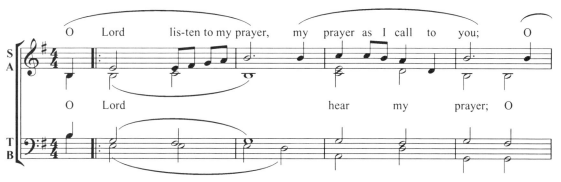

VARIATIONS FOR ORGAN/KEYBOARD (if there are no instruments available)
Variation 1

Variation 2

C INSTRUMENTS

Variation 1

Variation 2

Duet

B♭ INSTRUMENT VARIATION

'QUINTET': 24 BARS

PATTERN:

1) **SOLO 8 BARS**
2) **DUET 8 BARS**
3) **QUINTET 8 BARS**
(or may be used as solo variations)

Solo C instrument

DUET with 2 C instruments or 1 C instrument and 1 B♭ instrument

C inst.

either 2nd
C inst.

or
B♭ inst.

'QUINTET' with optional B♭ instrument and Celli

CELLI

Basso continuo 1

Basso continuo 2

'QUINTET'

Cello variation

GUITAR

Accompaniment 1

Accompaniment 2

Light in Our
Darkness

VENI SANCTE SPIRITUS

Text: Traditional
Music: Margaret Rizza

ORGAN/ELECTRIC KEYBOARD AND GUITAR

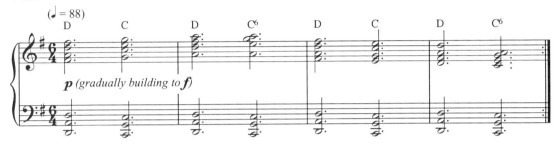

ORGAN VARIATION

CHANT TRIO: add a part on each repetition

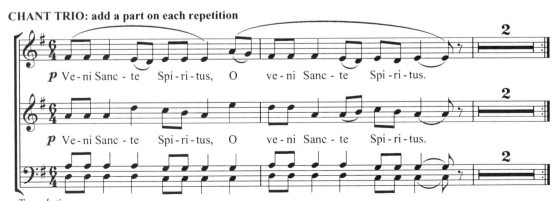

Translation:
Come, Holy Spirit,
O Come, Holy Spirit.

VOCAL ACCOMPANIMENT

Sanc - te Spi - ri - tus, O ve - ni, ve - ni

*p (2nd time **mp**)*

Sanc - te Spi - ri - tus, O ve - ni, O ve - ni.

Sanc - te Spi - ri - tus, O ve - ri - tus, O ve - ni, ve - ni

cresc.

Sanc - te Spi - ri - tus, O ve - ni, O ve - ni

Sanc - te Spi - ri - tus, Sanc - te Spi - ri - tus,

Sanc - te Spi - ri - tus, O ve - ni, O ve - ni.
mp　　　　　　　　　　*dim.*

C INSTRUMENT

Duet with Cello or Solo

p

mp　　　　　　　　*mf*

mp　　　*dim.*

2 C INSTRUMENTS or

1 C INSTRUMENT AND 1 B♭ INSTRUMENT

Variation duet or solo

C inst.

either 2nd
C inst.

or
B♭ inst.

METALLOPHONE

Variation 1

Variation 2

Variation 3

84

Variation 4:
either

or

CELLI

Basso continuo 1

Basso continuo 2

Variation: Duet with C instrument or Solo

I WILL BLESS THE LORD

Text: from Psalm 33(34), adapted from The Grail
Music: Margaret Rizza

boast and the hum - ble shall hear and be glad.

Unison or SATB

1. Glo - ri - fy the Lord with me, to - geth - er let us praise his

name; I sought the Lord and he ans - wered me, from

all my ter - rors he set me free. I will bless the Lord at all

times, his praise al - ways on my lips; in the

Lord my soul shall make its boast and the hum - ble shall hear and be

glad.

2. Look to-ward him and be ra - diant, let your fa - ces shine with

light. I called to the Lord and he heard me and

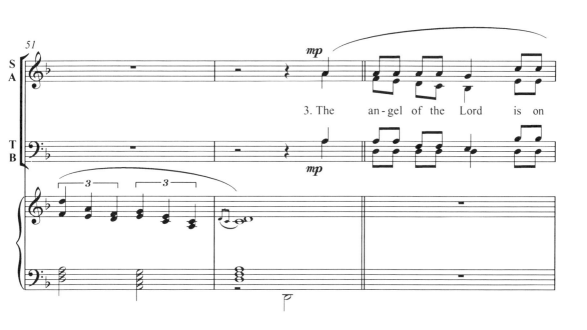

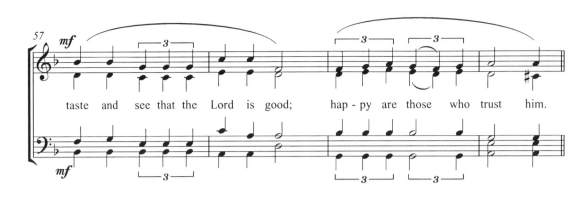

taste and see that the Lord is good; hap-py are those who trust him.

Refrain
Descant voices

I will bless the Lord,

SATB unison

I will bless the Lord at all times, his

bless the Lord, bless the

praise al-ways on my lips; in the Lord my soul shall make its

Other titles by Margaret Rizza

Fountain of Life

Cassette	1480040
CD	1490024
Full Score	1400147
Vocal Score	1450090
Melody edition	1400148

Fire of Love

Cassette	1480052
CD	1490036
Full Score	1400194
Vocal Score	1450114
Melody edition	1400195

River of Peace

Cassette	1480065
CD	1490050
Full Score	1400221
Vocal Score	1400222

Contemplative Choral Music

Music Book	1450117

Chants and Songs

Cassette	1480056
CD	1490040
Music Book	1450121

UNISON ✓
DESCANT ✓
OPTIONAL INSTRUMENTS ✓
FREE CD

Mass of the Bread of Life

Music Book   1450110

UNISON ✓
SATB ✓
OPTIONAL INSTRUMENTS ✓
FREE CD

Broken for You

Catholic   1450222
Anglican   1450221

Be Still and Know

Words Only   1413161
Full Music   1413162

Proclaiming God's Word

1500234

Choral Singles

Christus Natus Est
Lovely in Your Littleness